Sky Tales

by Michael Burgan
illustrated by Andrea Wesson

Chapters

Harcourt

Orlando   Boston   Dallas   Chicago   San Diego

Visit *The Learning Site!*
www.harcourtschool.com

Introduction

People today know many things about what we see in the sky. Scientists have studied our solar system. We have learned much about the sun, the moon, the stars, and the planets. We even know about solar wind, a stream of tiny particles flowing from the sun into space.

Astronauts have traveled to the moon and brought back rocks for scientists to study. Using telescopes and computers, we have explored the stars and planets. We learn more and more about space each day.

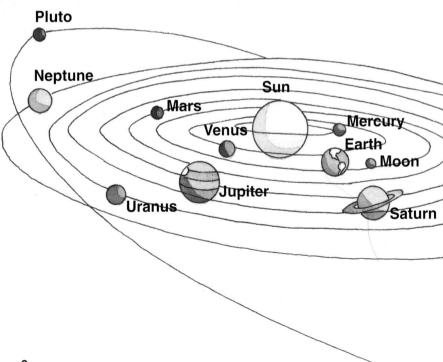

People have always wondered about the sun, the moon, and the stars. They have thought about the sun and how it acts as the nucleus, or center, of the solar system. They have wondered about what makes the sun rise and set. They have watched the moon and the stars on clear nights. They have been fascinated by the changes they have seen.

Long ago people didn't know very much about space. Storytellers made up tales to explain what they saw in the sky. Here are three tales about the sun, the moon, and the stars.

Four Men and the Moon —

Once there was a land that had no moon. After the sun had set, the country was covered in darkness. Four men from this land traveled to a nearby country. When the sun went down, they were amazed to see a dim light shine through the night.

"It is not daylight," said one man, "but it is not darkness either."

The men stopped a farmer coming down the road. "Where is that light coming from?" one man asked him.

"It's the moon," the farmer replied. "Our mayor bought it and hung it in an oak tree. We fill it with oil so it glows all night."

After the farmer went on his way, the four men decided to take the moon home with them. They climbed the tree, made a hole in the moon, and put loops of rope through the hole. Then they pulled the moon down and hauled it home in a cart.

Back home the four men hung the moon in an oak tree. All their neighbors were happy when they saw the moon's light. Even on foggy nights the moon's light was dimly fluorescent.

The townspeople loved the moon's light. In the evening they could visit their neighbors and find their way home. They paid the four men to keep the moon filled with oil.

Time passed. The four men had taken care of the moon for years. Now they were tired of doing that task. One day they let all the oil burn away. The night sky was dark once again.

What had happened? the townspeople wondered. Where had the moon gone? Only one young boy knew. He had watched his father take care of the moon for years.

The boy filled the moon with oil, and once again the moon lit up the night sky. The boy knew what to do so the night sky would not be dark again. With all his strength he threw the moon up into the sky. A mysterious force kept it there. From that day on, no one has had to take care of the moon. It has been shining brightly ever since.

Star Money ～

Once upon a time a young woman lived in a small cottage at the edge of a town. One day she went to look for work. A kindly baker offered her work in his shop. Her first day was filled with new experiences. She loved the smell of freshly baked bread.

On her way home, she walked along the icy road. It was winter, so she had on her plain woolen coat and her old red mittens. In her pocket was a piece of bread.

As she walked, she hummed. She had stopped to look at a tiny sparrow, when an old woman came up to her.

"Do you have a piece of bread for a very hungry woman?" the old woman asked. Then she added, "Please."

The young woman reached into her pocket and pulled out her piece of bread. "This is my only piece, but you are welcome to have it."

"Thank you for your kindness," cried the old woman. "I'll not forget it."

The young woman walked on. She was looking up at a puffy white cloud when she noticed a girl who had no coat.

"Aren't you very cold?" she asked.

"Yes, I am," the girl replied. "Do you have something for me to put on?" she asked. Then she added, "Please."

The young woman took off her woolen coat. She said, "This is my only coat, but you are welcome to have it."

"Thank you for your kindness," cried the girl. "I'll not forget it."

The young woman had hardly gone much farther when she saw a boy whose hands were red with cold. He just looked up at her.

The young woman looked at the boy. Then, without even saying a word, she slipped off her old red mittens and offered them to him.

"Thank you very much," said the boy. "My hands are so cold. I'll not forget your kindness."

By now it was dark, and the young woman was almost home. She looked up and noticed the stars that filled the sky. She had not seen the stars all day, but they had seen her. Suddenly, the stars began to fall from the sky. As they fell, the stars became golden coins.

The young woman saw that on her hands were her old red mittens. She wore her woolen coat, too. In her pocket was a piece of bread, which she quickly ate. She filled her empty pockets with the money and hummed as she walked home.

How Sun, Moon, and Wind Went Out to Dinner

One day Sun, Moon, Wind, and their mother (Star) were invited to dinner. They were invited to the home of Thunder and Lightning. Star was not feeling well and decided to stay home.

Sun and Wind couldn't wait for the huge feast they knew Thunder and Lightning would serve. When they all had arrived, Sun and Wind began to eat. Being greedy, they filled their plates with huge amounts of food. Being selfish, they did not think about their mother.

Moon was neither greedy nor selfish. Each time
she took a little food, she placed some in her pocket
for Star. When the feast was over, Thunder and
Lightning said good night. They asked Sun, Wind,
and Moon to send their good wishes to Star.

When they returned home, Star was awake. She
had been watching them from afar. She asked Sun
and Wind whether they had brought anything home
for her. They said they had not.

"Well, my dear Moon," Star said, "have you
brought anything home for me?"

"Why yes, Mother," said Moon, as she brought out wonderful treats.

Star spoke to Sun. "Because you did not remember your mother," she said, "you shall be punished. From now on your rays will be very hot. People will look away from you when you appear."

"Wind," Star said, "because you did not remember your mother, you shall be punished. From now on your wind will be very cold. People will turn away from you when you appear."

Then she smiled at Moon and said, "Moon, you were so kind to remember me. I was quite ill and needed food."

She thought for a minute and said, "Because you were so kind, you shall forever have a place in the night sky. You will be beautiful and bright. People will love your company and turn to you for light."

From that day on, Sun, Wind, and Moon lived just that way.